Leadership is Personal - Issue 1.0

KEVIN D WRIGHT
An aeriis company

302.588.5584
journey@kevindwright.com
www.kevindwright.com

You ever wish you had more? More money, more influence or just more time to do what you want to do? Do you ever worry you're not maximizing your full potential? What if I told you between these pages lies the secrets to abundance; to getting all you desire?

Engage in this journey and you'll learn how to get the most out of yourself and others, drive outcomes and be the best you imaginable. You'll have the money, power and respect you always dreamed of.

Before we dig in, I want to share a bit of perspective of why I wrote this book-journal. I was just an ordinary kid, growing up in Philadelphia, spending weekends at my grandmother's home in Springfield, Pennsylvania and every summer on my aunt and uncle's tobacco farm in Palmer Springs, Virginia. We didn't have much. But there was one thing I was sure of. I was enough. Growing up in the inner city, there were many that didn't hear this, never knew this, or didn't believe this. Today, I'm still just an ordinary man. However, I've been blessed to be able to do some extraordinary things. So from the vantage of a young boy, that recalls putting bread bags on his feet over his socks to keep his feet from getting wet through the holes in his shoes, turned corporate executive, writer and lover of all things people, I scribe this battle-tested plan of action that's been used to drive multi-million dollar organizations. I'm going to let you in on a little secret. The power to be everything you wish to be, is currently inside of you. "You are enough!"

The content could have been buried in a 60,000-word, 18 Chapter book requiring dense reading to capture the secrets. But in the words of some reality show, housewife-esque dialect, "Ain't nobody got time for that!" The format of this book-journal was created with insight and action as the objective. There is minimal reading of just a few pages to understand how to engage.

That's it. Each element is covered with a few checkpoints and primer questions so you get the point. The rest of the book-journal is for you to drive change in your life!

You can have anything in life you want, as long as you're willing to run head-first through fear to get it. All anyone needs to attain a goal is a bit of tenacity, perseverance and a plan. If you have the first two, but not the last, this book-journal is your answer. If you have an existing plan, no worries. There is still great value to be had, I assure you. If you lack the first two, keep going.

It is our actions that drive our emotions; not the other way around.

Keep moving forward. You ever not feel like going to the gym, but muster up just enough energy to get there? Then while there, well into your workout, you realize just how good you feel and how glad you are that you went? Work the plan, and the tenacity and perseverance will show up. It is the activity that drove the emotion in the gym example. Keep going. You're enough! Leadership is personal. It starts with YOU.

So often you hear the old adage, "It's not a goal until it's written down." Writing your goals down are not enough.

The paper upon which goals are written, without a plan of action to reach them, make for great scrap paper.

In other words, without a plan to get to where you would like to be, it is unlikely you will ever get there. I've created The Leadership Is Personal book-journal to assist those that aspire to be the very best version of themselves and lead. I believe leadership is personal, and to be the best leader, we must first be great leaders of our own dreams, desires and destiny. That is why this model is applicable to both individual and leadership aspirations.

THE MODEL INTRODUCTION

DIMENSIONS

When setting out to accomplish anything, there has to be a destination, a route and an idea of how long it may take to arrive. It's also a good idea to have a system of measurement to assess appropriate advancement toward the target. As kids setting out with our parents on the car ride from Philadelphia to the family's farm in Virginia, we looked forward to a stop at the Maryland House. Maryland is between Philadelphia and Virginia. While we may not have known how to drive or how exactly to get to Virginia, there were a few landmarks that provided an indication we were heading in the right direction. Unlike us, you are driving. As you embark on your journey to the best you, be certain to identify landmarks that indicate you're heading in the right direction. Remember road trips you took with your family as a youngster. Like those good times had during your road trips as a youngster, you will again enjoy the anticipation, progress and joy of arrival on your journey to the best you.

In the quest to be the very best version of yourselves, to drive change, improvement & maximization of capability in your life, you must have a frame of focus.

You may have heard colleagues and friends talking of a desire to be the very best version of themselves. But how? A wonderful endeavor indeed, albeit broad and far-reaching. Commendable? Yes. But where should they focus to be able to say they are striving to be their best? Where exactly should the focus be? Now you can tell them.

There are five core areas of focus for driving the very best in yourself and those you lead and influence. These five areas of focus are called Dimensions.

PROFESSIONAL | RELATIONAL | COMMUNITY | FINANCIAL | WELLNESS

These Dimensions were the foundation of focus when engaging those I led and influenced, as together we drove a less than one hundred million-dollar business to over 200 million dollars in revenue. Sure, we enjoyed unprecedented growth. But more than that, we enjoyed the company of and working with one another. It was this focus on the people and their 5 Dimensions that drove deeper connection, real engagement and meaning. Herb Kelleher said it best when he said, "The business of business is people." Take care of the people and in turn, the work will get taken care of. To be at your best, you cannot focus on only yourself.

> ### *Life is a "team sport." You can't play the game of life and leadership alone.*

Take care of the little things and the big things will take care of themselves. Leadership is personal. For you to maximize your capabilities, you must assist others maximize their capabilities.

It's difficult to read an article on human resources in the newspaper or LinkedIn and not read of the employee engagement issues the world is experiencing. Many are aware of the dearth in employee engagement that's prevalent across the US. Gallup reported roughly les than 30% of the US workforce is engaged. Focus on Dimensions is how you you drive engagement; those areas that give life meaning. Drive a vision for your life in each of the Dimensions.

Assist those you lead and influence to drive a vision in each of the Dimensions. Discuss them. Measure their progress. Assist in their advancement and you will get more out of your life and the people you lead and influence.

It used to be leadership could focus solely on the operations, profits and losses of business.

There's been a bit of a shift in the requirements of professional performance and leadership in the past decade or two. I recall complaining to my father about a Manager early in my career. His response, "If you like your boss, then he's doing something wrong." This approach to leadership has changed. The paradigm has shifted and the new rule is "know me." "And, I want to know you." As a culture, Americans tend to be tied to their business cards. Continuously excelling and succeeding with new positions and promotions is the prevailing desire. How good "life" is can have a direct dependence on your professional life and it's progression. Consequently, we begin with Professional.

> ### *Review your relationships to ensure the cast of characters you align with and choose to give your time are the most appropriate for where you're headed and who you wish to be at your best.*

Because you are human, there are times of engaging in self-limiting beliefs, doubting of your abilities, or replaying prior bad experiences in your mind as support for not believing in yourself. For this reason, the Relational dimension is one of the most crucial of the five to get right. Who do you spend the bulk of your time with? Are these people uplifting? Do they help you to see your blind spots or blindly tell you to press on? Are they capable of supporting you when you're at your weakest and unable to support your own emotions? Or when you're at your strongest, do they help you to see that though you are riding high, you have barely tapped the surface of your greatest capabilities? Do they help you to continue moving when you think you have nothing left to give? Do they help you aim higher and reach higher when you think you've already peaked?

Who is your Top-5?

Your five closest friends?

Humans are creatures of community and desire to share with others. We all desire the company of those with common characteristics or interests that makes us and our community unique in some fashion. Whether building bridges to connect resources within a community or better impacting segments within a specific community, the focus is what are you supporting that's "bigger than you?"

Some have said, "Money is the root of all evil." Financial access enables the prosocial pursuit of community and experience. Though you needn't have a great deal of it to enjoy life, it does help.

Manage it wisely and you will enjoy the experiences that bind, create the stories that last and leave the legacy that lives beyond your years.

A wise man once said, "Money is much like bread on a "crap" sandwich. The more "bread" you have, the less crap you have to eat."

There are two components to the Wellness dimension that are to be considered; mental and physical. The physical is what we first see and as a culture, associate with self-love, success and happiness. However, the mental is equally if not more important to address. Interestingly, this culture puts a premium on looking your best. However, one can't ignore the effects of what's going on between the ears on their body. The brain can very easily make the body sick. It is the most powerful and intricate part of the human body. You must nourish it, exercise it and give it time to rest. Contrary to the wide thought untruth that we only use 10% of our brain, it is constantly at work and being tasked with the mundane to the extraordinary.

We must also nourish, exercise and give our bodies time to rest. Both will say when they have been overworked.

Unfortunately, neither is equally as informative when they have been underworked.

Typically, someone else will enlighten us to when this occurs. And yet again, I call into clarity why the Relational dimension is so important.

STRATEGY

To show you how the Strategy works, I'd like to tell you a story from my college days. I moved down the court with the majestic tempo of a panther. Dribbled right. Around the back past the defender to cut left. I dished to my guy coming up the right side via no-look pass, ah la Magic Johnson, who bounce passed it right back in the paint. Boom! I jammed the ball with the force of LeBron. As I landed, I saw Coach Collick motioning me to come over to him. There would be absolutely no problem at all if Coach Collick were my basketball coach at Delaware State. He was not. Unfortunately for me this day, he caught me yet again playing basketball. Coach Collick was my football coach. Still not a problem if I weren't on a full football scholarship to play at the Division 1AA, Delaware State University. I was. As if this doesn't sound grave enough, these facts were the least of my worries. You see, when I came down the court, dribbling with the imagined skill of an over-sized Steph Curry, every BIG man desires to bring the ball up, I had on a penny loafer. I know. I know. I said a penny loafer. Yes. I had on dress trousers, a buttoned down shirt and a penny loafer. Why you might ask was I wearing just one shoe? Because the other penny loafer didn't fit over my cast. Duh!

Just weeks prior I had broken my fourth and fifth metatarsal during a football game. I had a cast on my foot up to my calf. Interestingly enough, I could run again after about a week. Obviously, since I was just caught red-handed dunking a basketball, in the main gym, on the game floor. While I was on the football team, I loved the game of basketball more. As I headed over to see my football Coach, I couldn't imagine what the messaging would be. This time...

It was quite obvious by the tinted shade of red in his face, he was furious.

"Son! You're no damned basketball player! And you're barely a football player! I don't know why I waste my time with you! You're just squandering your opportunity Wright!" He said a few octaves above a normal tone.

But then, like when your Mother has "had it up to here" with you and her yell goes to a quiet calm and peaceful tone that lets you know she is through, he got quiet.

Note to self, "It just got real." You know what Wright, "I'm tired. That's it. I don't want to catch your ass on the court again. And you know what else. You ain't been getting in the weight room either; 4 times. Psst." He said in a quiet confidence while still pondering. "You know son. Everyone else will sign their scholarships before leaving. You son? You won't. And if you don't get in the weight room over the summer? There won't be a scholarship here for you when you get back. I promise you Wright. Don't unpack when you get back. Your ass may be leaving just as quick as you arrive." "If you don't get in the weight room over the summer, you're done here son." Somehow, I knew he meant every word he almost whispered. There were many times you'd hear him yell and scream.

But as the saying goes, "Don't worry when you're getting yelled at. Worry when you're not."

He was done yelling and screaming at me. He was just done.

It became all too clear when I received an official letter, on college stationary, letting me know I'd lose my football scholarship if I was caught playing basketball again. Funny. It was on the very same letterhead, the embossed stationary, my scholarship letter was on. This was serious. The "four times" Coach Collick mentioned was in reference to my 225 bench-press max. The most I could lift 225 pounds was four times. Now that's not too bad for a kicker. But for a D1 football playing, guard / tight end, that's on a full scholarship? That is simply horrendous! I was a waste in his eyes at this point. If I didn't run a 4.6 in 40 yards, I'd surely been gone. At 6'4" and 265 pounds, I was one of the quickest players on the team "off the ball." That means within roughly the first 3 yards, from the snap of the football. Quickness was my savior. But no longer would this be enough. I had to lift. And lift is what I did.

For all intents and purposes, my "profession" was a student athlete. But, in Coach's eyes, I was being paid to play football. That made me an athlete student. The Field I was to "work" on was the football field. Getting clear on where you want to "play" in your professional existence is of utmost importance. As you create in your mind the legacy you want to leave and what it will look like, this should help to center you on where you want to "play."

I knew that I had to have a scholarship when I returned. And not just have one, but to keep one. My parents couldn't afford to send me to school and pay the tuition. I had a responsibility to use my skills to cover the costs of college. I knew this going in and nothing had changed. I had to get in the weight room. However, I wasn't going to become an overnight gym rat. I needed to network with someone that loved the gym as much as I needed to learn to love the gym. I needed a connection. Someone that cared enough about and for me to give of their time and talents. Enter Kennard. Kenny was and to this day is a gym rat.

He was the connection that kept me going when I didn't think that I could.

He was the connection that helped to hold me accountable when I didn't want to be held accountable. He was the one that made the unassailable difference that ultimately impacted my trajectory. This is what the right network can do. They can provide support and guidance when you need it most. I didn't need help with Accounting or Finance. Classes came easily. But iron? It was my kryptonite. I'd have no need for my understanding of Accounting or Finance without Kenny's expertise on the bench at River's Gym. Whenever I'm back in Philadelphia, I ride down Germantown Avenue, bumping along the cobblestone street past the old gym, just to reminisce.

I knew my point of Differentiation. I was 6'4", 265 pounds and ran 40 yards in 4.6 seconds. That's one hell of a time for someone of my then more svelte stature. While I hadn't the desire to play at the next level, which irritated the hell out of my coaches and my father, these physical statistics were NFL worthy. Too bad that wasn't my dream; it was theirs. This point of differentiation was more than enough to qualify me as a good athlete and enable my graduation, debt-free. This was my goal. What is your Point of Differentiation? What value does it bring to your "employer?" What is it that you do or service you provide that is able to be capitalized on? It is essential you understand your value proposition.

There is no greater business model, than the business model You!

I left school that summer and sure enough, there was no scholarship to sign before leaving. My parents were never the wiser. I knew what I needed to do and I was committed to doing just that. I knew what field I would take. I had made the requisite network I needed to assist in my success.

I had little clue of what to do to ensure I was taking the appropriate steps or Sequence of Events to guaranteed success.

Kenny was essential in helping to lay out a plan of action that would all but ensure Coach would be chomping at the bit to have me sign. He devised a schedule that would have me lift two days, give my body a day to rest and hit it again for two consecutive days. I would do this over the entire summer. What is it that you are doing to move toward your goal? While lifting was essential, so was exercising, eating right and sleeping. Between Kenny and the Staff of River's Gym, they would ensure I had captured the Sequence of Events that would enable goal-crushing output. What steps are you taking to ensure you not only reach, but exceed your goal? With every few days over the summer, I would pump out another rep or two on the bench. This was feedback. This was progress.

How do you know the steps you're taking are the appropriate steps?

I did this all summer long. In August, as I headed back to football camp, I knew I had put in the work. I was ready. Are your steps battle tested? By whom? Through what? How will you know you're ready and guaranteed success?

One. Two. Three. Four. This was all that I could eek out before departing Del-State. But I was certain I'd be back. I'd make the Impact that I was supposed to; that I was destined to. With my speed, surely I could be an unassailable difference on the D1 team that enjoyed the distinction of being in the NCAA Top 10 D1AA football teams in the country. I wanted to make an impact and I now knew how. I simply had to execute. One. Two. Three. Four. Nine… I was making progress. All summer long. 225. Incline? 225. Decline? 225. I was a 225 pound lifting machine. This was the plan. One. Two. Three. Four. Fifteen… I was on my way.

Back on campus in August, it was time to show and prove my system had worked. Coach held to his word and my documents were ready to be signed. If! If I had held up to my side of the bargain. One. Two. Three. Four… Nine… Fifteen… Nineteen… Twenty-four… Twenty-nine… Thirty… Thirty-one! My model early on was battletested and succeeded. Long before I had named the model or perfected it, I had identified a method to meet my goal. What is your method? Over a summer, I executed the painless steps and the Impact speaks for itself. I went from maxing out 225 pounds on the bench just 4 times to 31. That's a 775% increase! What would you like to increase 775%? Now an increase in maximum lifting isn't enough by itself. But what it enabled me to do on the field is what enhanced my point of differentiation and made me a real special teams threat. After blocking many punts, I had carte blanche' for where I wanted to line up on punts and PATs. Imagine the excitement I felt when I ran onto the field that next homecoming and there it was! A King Sized bed sheet painting of me blocking a punt. That came with a number of accolades. Impact!

What's your plan to Impact your life or the lives of others?

What is it that you wish to accomplish? You can. **You are enough!** Apply the Strategy, the 5 painless steps, to each Dimension to drive real engagement and meaning in your life and the lives of those you lead and influence.

CHECKPOINTS

√ Whether you are looking to grow in your existing role, looking to move to a different position/industry

√ What is your professional brand?

√ Are you managing your professional brand?

√ The focus here is YOU and your professional aspirations

If you were leaving for a 2 week vacation tomorrow, what would you absolutely get done before leaving today?

How would you empower the people you lead?

What would happen if you did this today even though you're not going on vacation?

How would this make tomorrow more productive?

What 5 things should you do tomorrow following the same approach?

Think about what you do for a living and ask yourself (and those you lead) these 3 questions…

1. What should I **start doing** to be a better leader/me?

2. What should I **stop doing** to be a better leader/me?

3. What should I **never stop doing** to be a better leader/me?

What do you aspire to do professionally? Are you passionately pursuing that work?

What "work" do you passionately do for free? Could you be paid "enough" to make a living doing it?

Do you enjoy what you do for a living? What if you did more (less) of this work, how would you feel?

[RELATIONAL]

FOCUS ON YOU AND YOUR CLOSEST RELATIONSHIPS (SIGNIFICANT OTHER AND 5 CLOSEST FRIENDS; YOUR TOP-5)

LEADERSHIP *is* PERSONAL

TM

CHECKPOINTS

√ What relationships are you giving the greatest amount of time to?

√ Who do you surround yourself with (Top-5)?

√ How does your Top-5 support your efforts and how do you support theirs?

Who are the 5 most important people in your life? (For this question, we are addressing your peers. Feel free to include your children also.)

When was the last time you told them? Tell them now! (A simple sincere note card or text works just fine. Don't overthink it.)

This will have an immediate impact on not only them, but YOU.

As you think about your aspirations, what do you and your Top-5 talk about? Are they supportive?

Are you sharing your big dreams with small minds or are they on your level or higher-level thinkers?

Can your Top-5 help you reach your aspirations or connect you with those who can?

How do you leverage the relationship and reciprocate?

If you are always the smartest in the room, you need a new room.

_____

_____

_____

_____

_____

_____

_____

_____

LEADERSHIP *is* PERSONAL

PROFESSIONAL · RELATIONAL · COMMUNITY · FINANCIAL · WELLNESS

TM

CHECKPOINTS

√ Potentially driven by proximity, affinity, culture or otherwise, this dimension focuses on the desired outcomes of your efforts in impacting the broader community

√ Whether "building bridges" to connect resources within a community, or better impacting specific segments within a community, the focus is what are you supporting that's "bigger than you?"

√ "Be ashamed to die, until you've won some victory for humanity."
- Horace Mann

What of yourself are you giving without an expectation of direct return, but a return that makes the world a better place?

What are you supporting passionately that is bigger than you?

What do you care about?

If you had infinite resources, what would you do with your time?

How do you impact community today? Is there an opportunity to do more right now?

_____

_____

_____

_____

_____

_____

_____

_____

_____

CHECKPOINTS

√ What does the best financial YOU look like?

√ What might you be...
- Investing in
- Providing for yourself or those you are responsible for
- Championing financially

√ The focus of this dimension is ensuring the maximization of your financial self

√ Time is more valuable than money!

How much money did you make while sleeping last night?

What skills do you have that someone would be willing to pay for, but isn't your 9:00-to-5:00?

What will you do this week that moves you closer to making passive income?

Some project the stock market will not provide ongoing returns historically seen. How will you adjust, capitalize, continue growth?

What are your financial goals for the month / quarter / year?

Of the debt you have, how much of it is "good debt" and how do you plan to accelerate the elimination of debt?

_____

_____

_____

_____

_____

_____

_____

_____

[WELLNESS]

CHECKPOINTS

√ What is your sense of meaning and purpose?

√ How do you recharge your batteries?
- Relaxation / meditation
- Worship / religious study
- Working out / yoga
- Running / walking

√ "It is better to ponder the meaning of life for ourselves and to be tolerant of the beliefs of others than to close our minds and become intolerant." National Wellness Institute

We are products of our experiences.

Statistically, most people wake up and grab their mobile device. Fight the urge. Begin each morning with thoughts of gratitude first (before grabbing the mobile device).

How much time have you spent being still and contemplating why you are here; your purpose?

Have you created a vision of what your best self looks like and a sense of purpose for your life? Do it! Use this journal and do it!

What is your ultimate purpose as you recall Horace Mann's words? "You should be ashamed to die until you've won some victory for mankind."

What are your limiting beliefs? Write them down. Now right down the truth about those limiting beliefs. I'd bet when you really consider your negative thinking about yourself, it's not totally true.

This game called life presents us with innumerable opportunities to be our best. Keep score! Have fun! Win!

_____

_____

_____

_____

_____

_____

[FIELDS]

TM

CHECKPOINTS

√ Identify where you wish to participate:
  • What industry?
  • What sector/segments?
  • What products?
  • What markets?

√ Where do you want to have the greatest impact?

√ What is your desired span of control; direct and influenced impact?

First, remove money from the equation. While it's a consideration, don't make it your first consideration.

What roles do you see yourself in? What identity do you aspire to in your profession?

What are your gifts? Ask your 5 closest friends/associates for their insight.

What topics do you argue or defend vigorously based on your core beliefs? What 3 roles would enable you to harness and leverage your core beliefs?

What work in your current role would you do for free?

When you're "in the zone" and lose all track of time and space, what are you doing?

_____

_____

_____

_____

_____

_____

_____

_____

_____

[NETWORKS]

IDENTIFY WITH WHOM AND THE METHODS UTILIZED TO BUILD RELATIONSHIPS.

CHECKPOINTS

√ With whom or what networks do you need to make connection, build relationships or gain exposure to move along your journey
  - Industry Associations
  - Colleges/Universities
  - Thought Leaders
  - Organizational Leaders (inside or out side of your organization
  - Divisional Managers
  - Clergy

√ Specific dimension will dictate where connections should be made to facilitate your moving along your journey

√ Life is a "team sport." You can't play the game of life and leadership alone

Once you know where you wish to engage, you can begin to identify the networks necessary to advance your mission. The key is first adding value for them. Then you can identify an exchange of value.

How will I add value for the person/organization that I wish to connect with?

Who in my current network can make a warm introduction to those identified?
Who can transfer relationship capital?

Who in my current network would be of value to the person/organization that I wish to connect with? Can I make a warm introduction to add value for them?

What help do I need from the person/organization? How do I communicate this succinctly and clearly, making it easy for them to engage and assist me?

Don't neglect to leverage social Media as a means of expanding your network beyond first and second level personal connections. Identify those that can be helpful in your mission and "follow" them, "like" them, "retweet" them and reach out to them.
Remember the idea is to add value for them.

$\left[\text{DIFFERENTIATORS} \right]$ IDENTIFY YOUR DISTINCT CHARACTERISTICS THAT ADD VALUE

TM

CHECKPOINTS

√ What is it that you bring to the challenge/equation/interaction that adds or enhances value?

√ What is your contributive value?
 • Proprietary knowledge/insight
 • Subject Matter Expertise
 • Emotional Intelligence
 • Relationships
 • Influence

√ Think of yourself as a brand. Your education, personality and experiences help you to stand out and add value

What from your education, experiences or background is leveragable that makes you better than the competition. For example, the following would be a differentiator for the person aspiring to lead a private security force. If applying for the role of VP Private Security, she might state the following... A former Marine Captain and combat Company leader, my military leadership skills and combat experience makes me battle-tested and better at leading a team of private security personnel for foreign dignitaries.)

What are the attributes and competencies valued by your organization? Careful to identify which attributes and characteristics are rewarded, versus those articulated or marketed as valued in the event there is a difference.

The key here is "differentiation" in the eye of the beholder. Care should be taken to understand the role of branding in this element of the strategy. You are the CEO of your number one business enterprise, *YOU Incorporated.*

What are the attributes of your brand. What do I get when I get *YOU Incorporated?*

A fast way to articulate your brand to those outside of your immediate circle is via social media. Manage the brand of *YOU Incorporated* diligently.

[SEQUENCE]

CHECKPOINTS

√ What are the time-bound steps that need to occur to move you from where you are today to where you aspire to be

  • e.g. At least once every two weeks sincerely tell my wife how much she means to me

√ Reverse engineer what it will take to get to your desired position in your profession, your relationship or your finances

√ Capture the steps necessary to achieve your goal and add time limits to achieving each step

STEP/TIME

There are two keys to Sequence; Steps and Time

For example, how many people will you have to connect with to get an introduction to the CEO you need to connect with?

For example, XYZ Company is in need of a new VP of Sales for their Foreign Dignitary Private Security Force. As a former Marine Captain and combat Company leader, with international combat experience, you're likely the best candidate. But applying on-line is not the best approach. You've identified an SVP at XYZ Company that your brother's manager used to work with.

• Advise brother of your revelation (by when_____)
• Get brother to introduce you to his manager (by when_____)
• Connect with brother's manager (by when_____)
• Research XYZ Company and cursory research of brother's company (by when_____)
• Research to learn about brother's manager (by when_____)
• Meet with brother's manager (by when_____)
• Get warm introduction to XYZ Company SVP (by when_____)
• Connect with SVP (by when_____)
• Apply (by when_____)

STRATEGY

[IMPACT]

TM

CHECKPOINTS

√ Create a clear vision for your life with meaning and purpose

√ Demonstrated ability to execute leadership models

√ Become a better leader by gaining a deeper understanding of those you lead and influence, understanding their differences, similarities and clear insight to motivations

It is through working the system that you gain the self-awareness, insight and vision to enable enhanced leadership and model application capability. You are then able to impact the lives of those you lead by providing a model for enhanced engagement and enlightenment.

This system drives real engagement and meaning in your life and the lives of those you lead and influence. Gallup indicates >70% of the US workforce is disengaged. Are you ensuring you're engaged? Are you applying what you've experienced to engage those you lead?

Are you using the system to create a clear vision, drive purposeful work, and create abundance? You are equipped to drive real engagement and meaning in the lives of others in profound ways?

What is your vision for your best you in each of the Dimensions? What are you doing specifically and how are you measuring success? Who are you impacting? How are you making the world a better place?

_____

_____

_____

_____

_____

_____

_____

_____

_____

$\left[\text{NOTES/REFLECTIONS}\right]$

KEVIN D WRIGHT
An aeriis company

302.588.5584
journey@kevindwright.com
www.kevindwright.com

HOW TO USE THE BOOK-JOURNAL

Beginning with the book, we look at the elements of the model and why use them. Briefly, we cover the Dimensions, what they are specifically and how they have been used to drive results in the past. Then a quick story to illustrate the Strategy and how its implemented in a fun way.

Each Dimension and Strategy element is presented on it's own page.

The journal portion of this book-journal provides the ability to drive real engagement and meaning in your life everyday by filling the pages and taking action.

Begin each day with gratitude. Research has shown that gratitude heightens quality of life. When you show gratitude, the recipient feels good. And so do you!

In fact, a study conducted by psychologists Michael McCollough and Robert Emmons showed keeping a daily journal of gratitude resulted in less depression and stress, greater likelihood to help others and more progress toward achieving personal goals.

Succinctly, you'll be happier. And happier people are more attractive, fun and engaging. At least from my perspective they are. We begin and end each day with gratitude in mind. It'll also help you rest better.

We wished to provide some structure, but not to attempt to over-engineer your day. Specific meetings can be captured in whatever calendar you use to track your minute-by-minute time. We've simply provided space for the "big rocks."

It was once said by First Lady Eleanor Roosevelt,

"You should do one thing everyday that scares you."

The attempt here is to move out of your comfort zone. The work of this book is about driving real engagement, meaning an abundance. Let's plant new memories of self-supporting wins in your mind. An old man once said to me, "If you always do, what you've always done, then you'll always get, what you've always gotten."

You can have anything you want in life, as long as you're willing to run head-first through fear to get it.

Stretch!

At the top of each second page for the day is a space to list which Dimension and which Strategy element will be focused on. Take care to capture what's done and the outcomes. Over time you will have a plethora of outcomes and be able to tell what specifically works for you.

Again not over-engineering your day, loads of space are provided to capture the most important tasks to get done, ideas and notes.

End each day with a check-in to capture new knowledge and close it out with gratitude.

Gratitude is good for the soul.

I wish you much success as you drive real engagement and meaning in your life!

I am grateful for *good health & the love of my family. Last nights mac & cheese! ☺ mmm*

"You can have anything in life you want, as long as you're willing to run head-first through fear and hard work to get it."

Kevin D. Wright

Morning:
meditate 15 minutes
pack for flight
Board mtg 3 days

Afternoon:
4/10 Lunch mtg agenda
New strategy presentation

shock

Supp. data

What will WOW the Management Committee in just 2 slides?

Evening:
pick up flowers tonight
get Dani a cake - Shrek

Call Mom & Dad

☐ What will I do today that scares me, but stretches me? Get out of my comfort zone!
Send email & call (2) angel investors requesting meetings. My idea is awesome!

☑ I extended compliment(s) *"I Love the way you think!" Daryl*
☑ I extended gratitude *"Couldn't do it without you! Felicia*
☑ I gave when no one was looking *bought coffee - Caribou drive then*

I am grateful for

"You can have anything in life you want, as long as you're willing to run head-first through fear and hard work to get it."

Kevin D. Wright

Morning:

Afternoon:

LEADERSHIP IS PERSONAL

Evening:

☐ What will I do today that scares me, but stretches me? Get out of my comfort zone!

A BETTER WORLD – A BETTER ME!

☐ I extended compliment(s)

☐ I extended gratitude

☐ I gave when no one was looking

Dimension _____ Strategy _____

Activities: _____

_____

_____

Outcome: _____

_____

_____

Must Do's

Notes:

What I learned today: _____

_____

Tonight's positive thoughts: _____

_____

I am grateful for _____

_____

"Everyone who wears your uniform, is not always on your team."

Anton Vincent

Morning:

_____

_____

_____

_____

Afternoon:

_____

LEADERSHIP IS PERSONAL

_____

_____

Evening:

_____

_____

_____

_____

☐ What will I do today that scares me, but stretches me? Get out of my comfort zone!

_____

_____

A BETTER WORLD – A BETTER ME!

☐ I extended compliment(s) _____

☐ I extended gratitude _____

☐ I gave when no one was looking _____

Dimension _____ Strategy _____

Activities: _____

_____

_____

Outcome: _____

_____

_____

Must Do's

Notes:

What I learned today: _____

_____

Tonight's positive thoughts:_____

_____

I am grateful for_____

_____

"What good is a soul, if your dare not to love?"

Kevin D. Wright

Morning:

_____

_____

_____

_____

Afternoon:

LEADERSHIP IS PERSONAL

_____

_____

Evening:

_____

_____

_____

_____

☐ What will I do today that scares me, but stretches me? Get out of my comfort zone!

_____

_____

A BETTER WORLD – A BETTER ME!

☐ I extended compliment(s)_____

☐ I extended gratitude _____

☐ I gave when no one was looking_____

Dimension _____Strategy _____

Activities: _____
_____
_____

Outcome: _____
_____
_____

Must Do's

Notes:

What I learned today: _____
_____

Tonight's positive thoughts:_____
_____

I am grateful for _____

_____

"If you stick with what you know, you will be stuck by what you know. Leaders must be life-long learners."

James Dallas

Morning:

_____

_____

_____

_____

Afternoon:

_____

LEADERSHIP IS PERSONAL

_____

_____

Evening:

_____

_____

_____

_____

☐ What will I do today that scares me, but stretches me? Get out of my comfort zone!

_____

_____

A BETTER WORLD – A BETTER ME!

☐ I extended compliment(s) _____

☐ I extended gratitude _____

☐ I gave when no one was looking _____

Dimension _____Strategy _____

Activities: _____

_____

_____

Outcome: _____

_____

_____

Must Do's

Notes:

What I learned today: _____

_____

Tonight's positive thoughts:_____

_____

I am grateful for _____

_____

For a gallant spirit there can never be defeat.

Wallis Simpson

Morning:

_____

_____

_____

_____

Afternoon:

_____

LEADERSHIP IS PERSONAL

_____

_____

Evening:

_____

_____

_____

_____

☐   What will I do today that scares me, but stretches me? Get out of my comfort zone!

_____

_____

A BETTER WORLD – A BETTER ME!

☐ I extended compliment(s) _____

☐ I extended gratitude _____

☐ I gave when no one was looking _____

Dimension _____Strategy _____

Activities: _____

_____

_____

Outcome: _____

_____

_____

Must Do's

Notes:

What I learned today: _____

_____

Tonight's positive thoughts:_____

_____

I am grateful for_____

_____

"Playing it safe is the biggest risk you'll ever take. Play to win."

Dawnna St. Louis

Morning:

_____

_____

_____

_____

Afternoon:

_____

LEADERSHIP IS PERSONAL

_____

_____

Evening:

_____

_____

_____

_____

☐   What will I do today that scares me, but stretches me? Get out of my comfort zone!

_____

_____

A BETTER WORLD – A BETTER ME!

☐ I extended compliment(s)_____

☐ I extended gratitude _____

☐ I gave when no one was looking _____

Dimension _____Strategy _____

Activities: _____

_____

_____

Outcome: _____

_____

_____

Must Do's

Notes:

What I learned today: _____

_____

Tonight's positive thoughts:_____

_____

I am grateful for _____

_____

Pride is holding your head up when everyone around you has theirs
bowed. Courage is what makes you do it.

Bryce Courtenay

Morning:

_____

_____

_____

_____

Afternoon:

_____

LEADERSHIP IS PERSONAL

_____

_____

Evening:

_____

_____

_____

_____

☐   What will I do today that scares me, but stretches me? Get out of my comfort zone!

_____

_____

A BETTER WORLD – A BETTER ME!

☐ I extended compliment(s)_____

☐ I extended gratitude _____

☐ I gave when no one was looking _____

Dimension _____ Strategy _____

Activities: _____

_____

_____

Outcome: _____

_____

_____

Must Do's

Notes:

What I learned today: _____

_____

Tonight's positive thoughts:_____

_____

We must change the subconscious mind that holds self-limiting beliefs that keep us from reaching our full potential. We must reprogram our minds so that subconsciously we begin to support, not sabotage our own success. Capture the negative self-limiting thoughts you tell yourself on the left side. List them all. Only after you have listed them, on the right side of the page, write the truth about each self-limiting thought.

Revisit this often, reminding yourself of the truth and how capable you are. Replace your self-limiting thoughts with reassuring self-thought.

Negative self-limiting thoughts	The positive truth

LEADERSHIP IS PERSONAL

Notes/Reflections:

I am grateful for_____

_____

Opportunities are seldom labeled.

Unknown

Morning:

_____

_____

_____

_____

Afternoon:

LEADERSHIP IS PERSONAL

_____

_____

Evening:

_____

_____

_____

_____

☐ What will I do today that scares me, but stretches me? Get out of my comfort zone!

_____

_____

A BETTER WORLD – A BETTER ME!

☐ I extended compliment(s)_____

☐ I extended gratitude _____

☐ I gave when no one was looking _____

Dimension _____ Strategy _____

Activities: _____

_____

_____

Outcome: _____

_____

_____

Must Do's

Notes:

What I learned today: _____

_____

Tonight's positive thoughts:_____

_____

I am grateful for_____

_____

Courage is like love: it must have hope for nourishment.

Napoleon

Morning:

_____

_____

_____

_____

Afternoon:

_____

LEADERSHIP IS PERSONAL

_____

_____

Evening:

_____

_____

_____

_____

☐   What will I do today that scares me, but stretches me? Get out of my comfort zone!

_____

_____

A BETTER WORLD – A BETTER ME!

☐ I extended compliment(s)_____

☐ I extended gratitude _____

☐ I gave when no one was looking _____

Dimension _____Strategy _____

Activities: _____

_____

_____

Outcome: _____

_____

_____

Must Do's

Notes:

What I learned today: _____

_____

Tonight's positive thoughts:_____

_____

I am grateful for _____

_____

Confidence is arrogance under control.

Walter Bond

Morning:

_____

_____

_____

_____

Afternoon:

LEADERSHIP IS PERSONAL

_____

_____

Evening:

_____

_____

_____

_____

☐   What will I do today that scares me, but stretches me? Get out of my comfort zone!

_____

_____

A BETTER WORLD – A BETTER ME!

☐ I extended compliment(s)_____

☐ I extended gratitude _____

☐ I gave when no one was looking _____

Dimension _____ Strategy _____

Activities: _____

_____

_____

Outcome: _____

_____

_____

Must Do's

Notes:

What I learned today: _____

_____

Tonight's positive thoughts:_____

_____

I am grateful for _____

_____

The world is a dinner table; you take all you want, but you better eat all you take.

John E. Vaughn

Morning:

_____

_____

_____

_____

Afternoon:

_____

LEADERSHIP IS PERSONAL

_____

_____

Evening:

_____

_____

_____

_____

☐   What will I do today that scares me, but stretches me? Get out of my comfort zone!

_____

_____

A BETTER WORLD – A BETTER ME!

☐ I extended compliment(s) _____

☐ I extended gratitude _____

☐ I gave when no one was looking _____

Dimension _____Strategy _____

Activities: _____

_____

_____

Outcome: _____

_____

_____

Must Do's

Notes:

What I learned today: _____

_____

Tonight's positive thoughts:_____

_____

I am grateful for _____

_____

Each mistake teaches you something new about yourself. There is no failure, remember, except in no longer trying. It is the courage to continue that counts.   Chris Bradford

Morning:

_____

_____

_____

_____

Afternoon:

_____

LEADERSHIP IS PERSONAL

_____

_____

Evening:

_____

_____

_____

_____

☐   What will I do today that scares me, but stretches me? Get out of my comfort zone!

_____

_____

A BETTER WORLD – A BETTER ME!

☐ I extended compliment(s)_____

☐ I extended gratitude _____

☐ I gave when no one was looking _____

Dimension _____ Strategy _____

Activities: _____

_____

_____

Outcome: _____

_____

_____

Must Do's

Notes:

What I learned today: _____

_____

Tonight's positive thoughts:_____

_____

I am grateful for_____

_____

It's not that people dislike change -- it's that they dislike not being a part of the change process.

Calvin Allen

Morning:

_____

_____

_____

_____

Afternoon:

_____

LEADERSHIP IS PERSONAL

_____

_____

Evening:

_____

_____

_____

_____

☐   What will I do today that scares me, but stretches me? Get out of my comfort zone!

_____

_____

A BETTER WORLD – A BETTER ME!

☐ I extended compliment(s)_____

☐ I extended gratitude _____

☐ I gave when no one was looking _____

Dimension _____ Strategy _____

Activities: _____

_____

_____

Outcome: _____

_____

_____

Must Do's

Notes:

What I learned today: _____

_____

Tonight's positive thoughts: _____

_____

I am grateful for _____

_____

If you knew everyone else's problems, you wouldn't complain about yours. You'd put yours in a bag and go on home.

Algie Wright

Morning:

_____

_____

_____

_____

Afternoon:

_____

LEADERSHIP IS PERSONAL

_____

_____

Evening:

_____

_____

_____

_____

☐ What will I do today that scares me, but stretches me? Get out of my comfort zone!

_____

_____

A BETTER WORLD – A BETTER ME!

☐ I extended compliment(s) _____

☐ I extended gratitude _____

☐ I gave when no one was looking _____

Dimension _____ Strategy _____

Activities: _____

_____

_____

Outcome: _____

_____

_____

Must Do's

Notes:

What I learned today: _____

_____

Tonight's positive thoughts:_____

_____

We must change the subconscious mind that holds self-limiting beliefs that keep us from reaching our full potential. We must reprogram our minds so that subconsciously we begin to support, not sabotage our own success. Capture the negative self-limiting thoughts you tell yourself on the left side. List them all. Only after you have listed them, on the right side of the page, write the truth about each self-limiting thought.

Revisit this often, reminding yourself of the truth and how capable you are. Replace your self-limiting thoughts with reassuring self-thought.

Negative self-limiting thoughts	The positive truth

LEADERSHIP IS PERSONAL

Notes/Reflections:

I am grateful for_____

_____

Your results are primarily determined by the depth of your reflection and quality of your relationships.

Ravi Norman

Morning:

_____

_____

_____

_____

Afternoon:

LEADERSHIP IS PERSONAL

_____

_____

Evening:

_____

_____

_____

_____

☐   What will I do today that scares me, but stretches me? Get out of my comfort zone!

_____

_____

A BETTER WORLD – A BETTER ME!

☐ I extended compliment(s)_____

☐ I extended gratitude _____

☐ I gave when no one was looking _____

Dimension _____ Strategy _____

Activities: _____

_____

_____

Outcome: _____

_____

_____

Must Do's

Notes:

What I learned today: _____

_____

Tonight's positive thoughts:_____

_____

I am grateful for _____

_____

Happiness is an inside job.

William Arthur Ward

Morning:

_____

_____

_____

_____

Afternoon:

_____

LEADERSHIP IS PERSONAL

_____

_____

Evening:

_____

_____

_____

_____

☐   What will I do today that scares me, but stretches me? Get out of my comfort zone!

_____

_____

A BETTER WORLD – A BETTER ME!

☐ I extended compliment(s)_____

☐ I extended gratitude _____

☐ I gave when no one was looking _____

Dimension _____Strategy _____

Activities: _____

_____

_____

Outcome: _____

_____

_____

Must Do's

Notes:

What I learned today: _____

_____

Tonight's positive thoughts:_____

_____

I am grateful for_____

_____

"It's not about you and your success, but your inspiration that helps others achieve success due to your impact on their lives."

Herschel Herndon

Morning:

_____

_____

_____

_____

Afternoon:

_____

LEADERSHIP IS PERSONAL

_____

_____

Evening:

_____

_____

_____

_____

☐   What will I do today that scares me, but stretches me? Get out of my comfort zone!

_____

_____

A BETTER WORLD – A BETTER ME!

☐ I extended compliment(s)_____

☐ I extended gratitude _____

☐ I gave when no one was looking _____

Dimension _____Strategy _____

Activities: _____

_____

_____

Outcome: _____

_____

_____

Must Do's

Notes:

What I learned today: _____

_____

Tonight's positive thoughts:_____

_____

I am grateful for _____

_____

"The greatest barrier to success is the fear of failure."

Sven Goran Eriksson

Morning:

_____

_____

_____

_____

Afternoon:

LEADERSHIP IS PERSONAL

_____

_____

Evening:

_____

_____

_____

_____

☐   What will I do today that scares me, but stretches me? Get out of my comfort zone!

_____

_____

A BETTER WORLD – A BETTER ME!

☐ I extended compliment(s)_____

☐ I extended gratitude _____

☐ I gave when no one was looking _____

Dimension _____ Strategy _____

Activities: _____

_____

_____

Outcome: _____

_____

_____

Must Do's

Notes:

What I learned today: _____

_____

Tonight's positive thoughts: _____

_____

I am grateful for_____

_____

"A leader is one who knows the way, goes the way, and shows the way."

John C. Maxwell

Morning:

_____

_____

_____

_____

Afternoon:

_____

LEADERSHIP IS PERSONAL

_____

_____

Evening:

_____

_____

_____

_____

☐ What will I do today that scares me, but stretches me? Get out of my comfort zone!

_____

_____

A BETTER WORLD – A BETTER ME!

☐ I extended compliment(s)_____

☐ I extended gratitude _____

☐ I gave when no one was looking _____

Dimension _____ Strategy _____

Activities: _____

_____

_____

Outcome: _____

_____

_____

Must Do's

Notes:

What I learned today: _____

_____

Tonight's positive thoughts: _____

_____

I am grateful for_____

_____

"Courage is going from failure to failure without losing enthusiasm."
Winston Churchill

Morning:

_____

_____

_____

_____

Afternoon:

_____

LEADERSHIP IS PERSONAL

_____

_____

Evening:

_____

_____

_____

_____

☐   What will I do today that scares me, but stretches me? Get out of my comfort zone!

_____

_____

A BETTER WORLD – A BETTER ME!

☐ I extended compliment(s)_____

☐ I extended gratitude _____

☐ I gave when no one was looking _____

Dimension _____ Strategy _____

Activities: _____

_____

_____

Outcome: _____

_____

_____

Must Do's

Notes:

What I learned today: _____

_____

Tonight's positive thoughts:_____

_____

I am grateful for _____

_____

"Dream as if you'll live forever, live as if you'll die today."

James Dean

Morning:

_____

_____

_____

_____

Afternoon:

_____

LEADERSHIP IS PERSONAL

_____

_____

Evening:

_____

_____

_____

_____

☐   What will I do today that scares me, but stretches me? Get out of my comfort zone!

_____

_____

A BETTER WORLD – A BETTER ME!

☐ I extended compliment(s)_____

☐ I extended gratitude _____

☐ I gave when no one was looking _____

Dimension _____ Strategy _____

Activities: _____

_____

_____

Outcome: _____

_____

_____

Must Do's

Notes:

What I learned today: _____

_____

Tonight's positive thoughts: _____

_____

We must change the subconscious mind that holds self-limiting beliefs that keep us from reaching our full potential. We must reprogram our minds so that subconsciously we begin to support, not sabotage our own success. Capture the negative self-limiting thoughts you tell yourself on the left side. List them all. <u>Only after you have listed them,</u> on the right side of the page, write the truth about each self-limiting thought.

Revisit this often, reminding yourself of the truth and how capable you are. Replace your self-limiting thoughts with reassuring self-thought.

Negative self-limiting thoughts	The positive truth

LEADERSHIP IS PERSONAL

Notes/Reflections:

I am grateful for _____

_____

"It does not matter how slowly you go as long as you do not stop."

Confucius

Morning:

_____

_____

_____

_____

Afternoon:

_____

LEADERSHIP IS PERSONAL

_____

_____

Evening:

_____

_____

_____

_____

☐   What will I do today that scares me, but stretches me? Get out of my comfort zone!

_____

_____

A BETTER WORLD – A BETTER ME!

☐ I extended compliment(s)_____

☐ I extended gratitude _____

☐ I gave when no one was looking _____

Dimension _____Strategy _____

Activities: _____

_____

_____

Outcome: _____

_____

_____

Must Do's

Notes:

What I learned today: _____

_____

Tonight's positive thoughts:_____

_____

I am grateful for _____

_____

The only things that happen naturally in an organization are friction, confusion, and malperformance. Everything else is the result of leadership.

Peter Drucker

Morning:

_____

_____

_____

_____

Afternoon:

LEADERSHIP IS PERSONAL

_____

_____

Evening:

_____

_____

_____

_____

☐   What will I do today that scares me, but stretches me? Get out of my comfort zone!

_____

_____

A BETTER WORLD – A BETTER ME!

☐ I extended compliment(s)_____

☐ I extended gratitude _____

☐ I gave when no one was looking _____

Dimension _____Strategy _____

Activities: _____

_____

_____

Outcome: _____

_____

_____

Must Do's

Notes:

What I learned today: _____

_____

Tonight's positive thoughts:_____

_____

I am grateful for _____

_____

You learn something new everyday if you pay attention.

Ray LeBlond

Morning:

_____

_____

_____

_____

Afternoon:

LEADERSHIP IS PERSONAL

_____

_____

Evening:

_____

_____

_____

_____

☐   What will I do today that scares me, but stretches me? Get out of my comfort zone!

_____

_____

A BETTER WORLD – A BETTER ME!

☐ I extended compliment(s) _____

☐ I extended gratitude _____

☐ I gave when no one was looking _____

Dimension _____ Strategy _____

Activities: _____

_____

_____

Outcome: _____

_____

_____

Must Do's

Notes:

What I learned today: _____

_____

Tonight's positive thoughts: _____

_____

I am grateful for _____

Life is too short to miss out on being truly happy.

Viral Patel

Morning:

_____

_____

_____

_____

Afternoon:

LEADERSHIP IS PERSONAL

_____

_____

Evening:

_____

_____

_____

_____

☐   What will I do today that scares me, but stretches me? Get out of my comfort zone!

_____

_____

A BETTER WORLD – A BETTER ME!

☐ I extended compliment(s) _____

☐ I extended gratitude _____

☐ I gave when no one was looking _____

Dimension _____ Strategy _____

Activities: _____
_____
_____

Outcome: _____
_____
_____

Must Do's

Notes:

What I learned today: _____
_____

Tonight's positive thoughts: _____
_____

I am grateful for_____

_____

Do not let the behavior of others destroy your inner peace.

Dalai Lama

Morning:

_____

_____

_____

_____

Afternoon:

_____

LEADERSHIP IS PERSONAL

_____

_____

Evening:

_____

_____

_____

_____

☐   What will I do today that scares me, but stretches me? Get out of my comfort zone!

_____

_____

A BETTER WORLD – A BETTER ME!

☐ I extended compliment(s)_____

☐ I extended gratitude _____

☐ I gave when no one was looking_____

Dimension _____ Strategy _____

Activities: _____

_____

_____

Outcome: _____

_____

_____

Must Do's

Notes:

What I learned today: _____

_____

Tonight's positive thoughts:_____

_____

I am grateful for_____

_____

We don't laugh because we're happy. We're happy because we laugh.

William Jones

Morning:

_____

_____

_____

_____

Afternoon:

LEADERSHIP IS PERSONAL

_____

_____

Evening:

_____

_____

_____

_____

☐   What will I do today that scares me, but stretches me? Get out of my comfort zone!

_____

_____

A BETTER WORLD – A BETTER ME!

☐ I extended compliment(s)_____

☐ I extended gratitude _____

☐ I gave when no one was looking _____

Dimension _____ Strategy _____

Activities: _____

_____

_____

Outcome: _____

_____

_____

Must Do's

Notes:

What I learned today: _____

_____

Tonight's positive thoughts: _____

_____

I am grateful for _____

_____

Those who think they have not time for bodily exercise will sooner or later have to find time for illness.

Edward Stanley

Morning:

_____

_____

_____

_____

Afternoon:

_____

LEADERSHIP IS PERSONAL

_____

_____

Evening:

_____

_____

_____

_____

☐   What will I do today that scares me, but stretches me? Get out of my comfort zone!

_____

_____

A BETTER WORLD – A BETTER ME!

☐ I extended compliment(s) _____

☐ I extended gratitude _____

☐ I gave when no one was looking _____

Dimension _____ Strategy _____

Activities: _____

_____

_____

Outcome: _____

_____

_____

Must Do's

Notes:

What I learned today: _____

_____

Tonight's positive thoughts: _____

_____

We must change the subconscious mind that holds self-limiting beliefs that keep us from reaching our full potential. We must reprogram our minds so that subconsciously we begin to support, not sabotage our own success. Capture the negative self-limiting thoughts you tell yourself on the left side. List them all. Only after you have listed them, on the right side of the page, write the truth about each self-limiting thought.

Revisit this often, reminding yourself of the truth and how capable you are. Replace your self-limiting thoughts with reassuring self-thought.

Negative self-limiting thoughts	The positive truth

LEADERSHIP IS PERSONAL

Notes/Reflections:

I am grateful for _____

_____

Only in a quiet mind is adequate perception of the world.

Hans Margolius

Morning:

_____

_____

_____

_____

Afternoon:

_____

LEADERSHIP IS PERSONAL

_____

_____

Evening:

_____

_____

_____

_____

☐   What will I do today that scares me, but stretches me? Get out of my comfort zone!

_____

_____

A BETTER WORLD – A BETTER ME!

☐ I extended compliment(s)_____

☐ I extended gratitude _____

☐ I gave when no one was looking _____

Dimension _____ Strategy _____

Activities: _____

_____

_____

Outcome: _____

_____

_____

Must Do's

Notes:

What I learned today: _____

_____

Tonight's positive thoughts: _____

_____

I am grateful for_____

Love yourself. Accept yourself. Forgive yourself.

Leo Buscaglia

Morning:

_____

_____

_____

_____

Afternoon:

_____

LEADERSHIP IS PERSONAL

_____

_____

Evening:

_____

_____

_____

_____

☐ What will I do today that scares me, but stretches me? Get out of my comfort zone!

_____

_____

A BETTER WORLD – A BETTER ME!

☐ I extended compliment(s)_____

☐ I extended gratitude _____

☐ I gave when no one was looking _____

Dimension _____ Strategy _____

Activities: _____

_____

_____

Outcome: _____

_____

_____

Must Do's

Notes:

What I learned today: _____

_____

Tonight's positive thoughts:_____

_____

I am grateful for _____

_____

Being happy doesn't mean that everything is perfect. It means that you've decided to look beyond the imperfections.

Unknown

Morning:

_____

_____

_____

_____

Afternoon:

LEADERSHIP IS PERSONAL

_____

_____

Evening:

_____

_____

_____

_____

☐   What will I do today that scares me, but stretches me? Get out of my comfort zone!

_____

_____

A BETTER WORLD – A BETTER ME!

☐ I extended compliment(s)_____

☐ I extended gratitude _____

☐ I gave when no one was looking _____

Dimension _____ Strategy _____

Activities: _____

_____

_____

Outcome: _____

_____

_____

Must Do's

Notes:

What I learned today: _____

_____

Tonight's positive thoughts:_____

_____

I am grateful for _____

_____

No act of kindness is ever wasted.

Aesop

Morning:

_____

_____

_____

_____

Afternoon:

_____

LEADERSHIP IS PERSONAL

_____

_____

Evening:

_____

_____

_____

_____

☐ What will I do today that scares me, but stretches me? Get out of my comfort zone!

_____

_____

A BETTER WORLD – A BETTER ME!

☐ I extended compliment(s) _____

☐ I extended gratitude _____

☐ I gave when no one was looking _____

Dimension _____ Strategy _____

Activities: _____
_____
_____

Outcome: _____
_____
_____

Must Do's

Notes:

What I learned today: _____
_____

Tonight's positive thoughts: _____
_____

I am grateful for _____

_____

You can't innovate what you can't imagine; dream.

Kevin D. Wright

Morning:

_____

_____

_____

_____

Afternoon:

_____

LEADERSHIP IS PERSONAL

_____

_____

Evening:

_____

_____

_____

_____

☐   What will I do today that scares me, but stretches me? Get out of my comfort zone!

_____

_____

A BETTER WORLD – A BETTER ME!

☐ I extended compliment(s)_____

☐ I extended gratitude _____

☐ I gave when no one was looking _____

Dimension _____ Strategy _____

Activities: _____

_____

_____

Outcome: _____

_____

_____

Must Do's

Notes:

What I learned today: _____

_____

Tonight's positive thoughts: _____

_____

I am grateful for _____

_____

When distractions come, remember what matters most to you.

Vicki Morris

Morning:

_____

_____

_____

_____

Afternoon:

LEADERSHIP IS PERSONAL

_____

_____

Evening:

_____

_____

_____

_____

☐   What will I do today that scares me, but stretches me? Get out of my comfort zone!

_____

_____

A BETTER WORLD – A BETTER ME!

☐ I extended compliment(s)_____

☐ I extended gratitude _____

☐ I gave when no one was looking _____

Dimension _____ Strategy _____

Activities: _____

_____

_____

Outcome: _____

_____

_____

Must Do's

Notes:

What I learned today: _____

_____

Tonight's positive thoughts:_____

_____

I am grateful for_____

_____

Setting goals is the first step to turning the invisible into the visible.

Tony Robbins

Morning:

_____

_____

_____

_____

Afternoon:

LEADERSHIP IS PERSONAL

_____

_____

Evening:

_____

_____

_____

_____

☐   What will I do today that scares me, but stretches me? Get out of my comfort zone!

_____

_____

A BETTER WORLD – A BETTER ME!

☐ I extended compliment(s)_____

☐ I extended gratitude _____

☐ I gave when no one was looking _____

Dimension _____ Strategy _____

Activities: _____

_____

_____

Outcome: _____

_____

_____

Must Do's

Notes:

What I learned today: _____

_____

Tonight's positive thoughts: _____

_____

We must change the subconscious mind that holds self-limiting beliefs that keep us from reaching our full potential. We must reprogram our minds so that subconsciously we begin to support, not sabotage our own success. Capture the negative self-limiting thoughts you tell yourself on the left side. List them all. Only after you have listed them, on the right side of the page, write the truth about each self-limiting thought.

Revisit this often, reminding yourself of the truth and how capable you are. Replace your self-limiting thoughts with reassuring self-thought.

Negative self-limiting thoughts	The positive truth

LEADERSHIP IS PERSONAL

Notes/Reflections:

I am grateful for _____

_____

It's not that some people have willpower and some don't. It's that some people are ready to change and others are not.

James Gordon

Morning:

_____

_____

_____

_____

Afternoon:

LEADERSHIP IS PERSONAL

_____

_____

Evening:

_____

_____

_____

_____

☐ What will I do today that scares me, but stretches me? Get out of my comfort zone!

_____

_____

A BETTER WORLD – A BETTER ME!

☐ I extended compliment(s) _____

☐ I extended gratitude _____

☐ I gave when no one was looking _____

Dimension _____ Strategy _____

Activities: _____

_____

_____

Outcome: _____

_____

_____

Must Do's

Notes:

What I learned today: _____

_____

Tonight's positive thoughts: _____

_____

I am grateful for _____

_____

The best feeling of happiness is when you're happy because you've made someone else happy.

Unknown

Morning:

_____

_____

_____

_____

Afternoon:

_____

LEADERSHIP IS PERSONAL

_____

_____

Evening:

_____

_____

_____

_____

☐ What will I do today that scares me, but stretches me? Get out of my comfort zone!

_____

_____

A BETTER WORLD – A BETTER ME!

☐ I extended compliment(s) _____

☐ I extended gratitude _____

☐ I gave when no one was looking _____

Dimension _____ Strategy _____

Activities: _____

_____

_____

Outcome: _____

_____

_____

Must Do's

Notes:

LEADERSHIP
is
PERSONAL

FIELDS

PROFESSIONAL

RELATIONAL

NETWORKS

IMPACT

WELLNESS

FINANCIAL

COMMUNITY

DIFFERENTIATORS

SEQUENCE

TM

What I learned today: _____

_____

Tonight's positive thoughts: _____

_____

I am grateful for_____

_____

Happiness means loving yourself and being less concerned with the approval of others.

Owen Campbell Jr.

Morning:

_____

_____

_____

_____

Afternoon:

_____

LEADERSHIP IS PERSONAL

_____

_____

Evening:

_____

_____

_____

_____

☐ What will I do today that scares me, but stretches me? Get out of my comfort zone!

_____

_____

A BETTER WORLD – A BETTER ME!

☐ I extended compliment(s)_____

☐ I extended gratitude _____

☐ I gave when no one was looking _____

Dimension _____Strategy _____

Activities: _____

_____

_____

Outcome: _____

_____

_____

Must Do's

Notes:

What I learned today: _____

_____

Tonight's positive thoughts: _____

_____

I am grateful for_____

_____

If you want to find happiness, find gratitude.

Steve Maraboli

Morning:

_____

_____

_____

_____

Afternoon:

LEADERSHIP IS PERSONAL

_____

_____

Evening:

_____

_____

_____

_____

☐   What will I do today that scares me, but stretches me? Get out of my comfort zone!

_____

_____

A BETTER WORLD – A BETTER ME!

☐ I extended compliment(s)_____

☐ I extended gratitude _____

☐ I gave when no one was looking _____

Dimension _____ Strategy _____

Activities: _____

_____

_____

Outcome: _____

_____

_____

Must Do's

Notes:

What I learned today: _____

_____

Tonight's positive thoughts:_____

_____

I am grateful for _____

_____

If you are not working on your ideal day, you are working on somebody else's.

Marjorie Blanchard

Morning:

_____

_____

_____

_____

Afternoon:

_____

LEADERSHIP IS PERSONAL

_____

_____

Evening:

_____

_____

_____

_____

☐ What will I do today that scares me, but stretches me? Get out of my comfort zone!

_____

_____

A BETTER WORLD – A BETTER ME!

☐ I extended compliment(s)_____

☐ I extended gratitude _____

☐ I gave when no one was looking _____

Dimension _____ Strategy _____

Activities: _____

_____

_____

Outcome: _____

_____

_____

Must Do's

Notes:

What I learned today: _____

_____

Tonight's positive thoughts:_____

_____

I am grateful for_____

_____

There are only two mistakes one can make along the road of truth; not going all the way, and not starting.

Buddha

Morning:

_____

_____

_____

_____

Afternoon:

_____

LEADERSHIP IS PERSONAL

_____

_____

Evening:

_____

_____

_____

_____

☐   What will I do today that scares me, but stretches me? Get out of my comfort zone!

_____

_____

A BETTER WORLD – A BETTER ME!

☐ I extended compliment(s)_____

☐ I extended gratitude _____

☐ I gave when no one was looking _____

Dimension _____Strategy _____

Activities: _____

_____

_____

Outcome: _____

_____

_____

Must Do's

Notes:

What I learned today: _____

_____

Tonight's positive thoughts:_____

_____

I am grateful for _____

_____

Great works are performed not by strength but by perseverance.

Samuel Johnson

Morning:

_____

_____

_____

_____

Afternoon:

_____

LEADERSHIP IS PERSONAL

_____

_____

Evening:

_____

_____

_____

_____

☐   What will I do today that scares me, but stretches me? Get out of my comfort zone!

_____

_____

A BETTER WORLD – A BETTER ME!

☐ I extended compliment(s) _____

☐ I extended gratitude _____

☐ I gave when no one was looking _____

Dimension _____ Strategy _____

Activities: _____

_____

_____

Outcome: _____

_____

_____

Must Do's

Notes:

What I learned today: _____

_____

Tonight's positive thoughts: _____

_____

We must change the subconscious mind that holds self-limiting beliefs that keep us from reaching our full potential. We must reprogram our minds so that subconsciously we begin to support, not sabotage our own success. Capture the negative self-limiting thoughts you tell yourself on the left side. List them all. <u>Only after you have listed them</u>, on the right side of the page, write the truth about each self-limiting thought.

Revisit this often, reminding yourself of the truth and how capable you are. Replace your self-limiting thoughts with reassuring self-thought.

Negative self-limiting thoughts	The positive truth

LEADERSHIP IS PERSONAL

Notes/Reflections:

I am grateful for

It is not ignorance but knowledge which is the mother of wonder.

Joseph Wood Krutch

Morning:

Afternoon:

LEADERSHIP IS PERSONAL

Evening:

☐   What will I do today that scares me, but stretches me? Get out of my comfort zone!

A BETTER WORLD – A BETTER ME!

☐ I extended compliment(s)

☐ I extended gratitude

☐ I gave when no one was looking

Dimension _____ Strategy _____

Activities: _____

_____

_____

Outcome: _____

_____

_____

Must Do's

Notes:

What I learned today: _____

_____

Tonight's positive thoughts: _____

_____

I am grateful for _____

_____

Give light and people will find the way.

Ella Baker

Morning:

_____

_____

_____

_____

Afternoon:

_____

LEADERSHIP IS PERSONAL

_____

_____

Evening:

_____

_____

_____

_____

☐   What will I do today that scares me, but stretches me? Get out of my comfort zone!

_____

_____

A BETTER WORLD – A BETTER ME!

☐ I extended compliment(s) _____

☐ I extended gratitude _____

☐ I gave when no one was looking _____

Dimension _____Strategy _____

Activities: _____

_____

_____

Outcome: _____

_____

_____

Must Do's

Notes:

What I learned today: _____

_____

Tonight's positive thoughts:_____

_____

I am grateful for _____

_____

Mankind is made great or little by its own will.

Friedrich Schiller

Morning:

_____

_____

_____

_____

Afternoon:

LEADERSHIP IS PERSONAL

_____

_____

Evening:

_____

_____

_____

_____

☐ What will I do today that scares me, but stretches me? Get out of my comfort zone!

_____

_____

A BETTER WORLD – A BETTER ME!

☐ I extended compliment(s)_____

☐ I extended gratitude _____

☐ I gave when no one was looking _____

Dimension _____Strategy _____

Activities: _____

_____

_____

Outcome: _____

_____

_____

Must Do's

Notes:

What I learned today: _____

_____

Tonight's positive thoughts:_____

_____

I am grateful for _____

_____

Your future is created by what you do today not tomorrow.

Unknown

Morning:

_____

_____

_____

_____

Afternoon:

LEADERSHIP IS PERSONAL

_____

_____

Evening:

_____

_____

_____

_____

☐ What will I do today that scares me, but stretches me? Get out of my comfort zone!

_____

_____

A BETTER WORLD – A BETTER ME!

☐ I extended compliment(s) _____

☐ I extended gratitude _____

☐ I gave when no one was looking _____

Dimension _____ Strategy _____

Activities: _____

_____

_____

Outcome: _____

_____

_____

Must Do's

Notes:

What I learned today: _____

_____

Tonight's positive thoughts:_____

_____

I am grateful for _____

_____

"Great leadership is like a large stone dropped in a body of water. It's ripple spans farther and wider than you'll ever see.

Milton Dodd

Morning:

_____

_____

_____

_____

Afternoon:

_____

LEADERSHIP IS PERSONAL

_____

_____

Evening:

_____

_____

_____

_____

☐   What will I do today that scares me, but stretches me? Get out of my comfort zone!

_____

_____

A BETTER WORLD – A BETTER ME!

☐ I extended compliment(s)_____

☐ I extended gratitude _____

☐ I gave when no one was looking _____

Dimension _____ Strategy _____

Activities: _____

_____

_____

Outcome: _____

_____

_____

Must Do's

Notes:

What I learned today: _____

_____

Tonight's positive thoughts:_____

_____

I am grateful for _____

_____

"Fears are present, within anyone and everyone, our minds use our fears to decide and act in life, imagine a fear into a passion and take the action to make a life change."   Tonya Hampton

Morning:

_____

_____

_____

_____

Afternoon:

_____

LEADERSHIP IS PERSONAL

_____

_____

Evening:

_____

_____

_____

_____

☐   What will I do today that scares me, but stretches me? Get out of my comfort zone!

_____

_____

A BETTER WORLD – A BETTER ME!

☐ I extended compliment(s)_____

☐ I extended gratitude _____

☐ I gave when no one was looking _____

Dimension _____ Strategy _____

Activities: _____

_____

_____

Outcome: _____

_____

_____

Must Do's

Notes:

What I learned today: _____

_____

Tonight's positive thoughts: _____

_____

I am grateful for _____

"I didn't begin to have professional success until I gained psychological safety, and gave myself permission for interpersonal risk taking. That sense of confidence that you will not be embarrassed, rejected, or punished for being who you are without compromise".   Greg Cunningham

Morning:

_____

_____

_____

_____

Afternoon:

_____

LEADERSHIP IS PERSONAL

_____

_____

Evening:

_____

_____

_____

_____

☐   What will I do today that scares me, but stretches me? Get out of my comfort zone!

_____

_____

A BETTER WORLD – A BETTER ME!

☐ I extended compliment(s) _____

☐ I extended gratitude _____

☐ I gave when no one was looking _____

Dimension _____ Strategy _____

Activities: _____

_____

_____

Outcome: _____

_____

_____

Must Do's

Notes:

What I learned today: _____

_____

Tonight's positive thoughts:_____

_____

We must change the subconscious mind that holds self-limiting beliefs that keep us from reaching our full potential. We must reprogram our minds so that subconsciously we begin to support, not sabotage our own success. Capture the negative self-limiting thoughts you tell yourself on the left side. List them all. <u>Only after you have listed them,</u> on the right side of the page, write the truth about each self-limiting thought.

Revisit this often, reminding yourself of the truth and how capable you are. Replace your self-limiting thoughts with reassuring self-thought.

Negative self-limiting thoughts	The positive truth

LEADERSHIP IS PERSONAL

Notes/Reflections:

LEADERSHIP *is* PERSONAL

KEVIN D. WRIGHT - Strategic Management Consultant/Speaker

A rare combination of strategic and analytical thinking with a love for disruptive innovation, ideals and people is who Kevin authentically is.

A seasoned executive with National & International broad-based leadership experience of ~20 years, he's Managing Partner of Aeriis (air'-ris) Inc., a strategic management consulting firm and holding company. Kevin spends the bulk of his time working with organizations that want to more deeply connect with and engage their employees and customers, reducing the high costs of developing, retaining and igniting top talent and customers. He is also an adjunct faculty member of the Hamline University, Graduate School of Business.

A former corporate Vice President and leader in corporate strategy, segmentation, product development, product management, revenue generation, expense management, Six Sigma and more. He was selected as one of the Top 40 Inspirers in America by Inspire Magazine," a publication designed to enhance the lives of leaders. Kevin sits on the Infinity Systems Board, Sunrise Banks Advisory Board and University of Minnesota, Office of Technology Commercialization, Business Advisory Group.

Kevin has been a speaker or panelist at a number of well known venues across the US. He has published a number of articles on employee engagement, development and leadership and has been interviewed by and/or quoted in The Wall Street Journal, American Banker, Franchise Times and more. Kevin holds an MBA from The Smeal College of Business at Pennsylvania State University, University Park, Pennsylvania and a B.S. in Business Administration from Delaware State University. A lover of education and people, he's also completed post-graduate studies in Counseling.

KEVIN D WRIGHT
An aeriis company

302.588.5584
journey@kevindwright.com
www.kevindwright.com